SIMPLE MACHINES
Force & Motion Series

• • • • • • • • • • • • • • • • • •

Written by George Graybill, Ph. D.

GRADES 5 - 8
Reading Levels 3 - 4

Classroom Complete Press

P.O. Box 19729
San Diego, CA 92159
Tel: 1-800-663-3609 / Fax: 1-800-663-3608
Email: service@classroomcompletepress.com

www.classroomcompletepress.com

ISBN-13: 978-1-55319-376-0
ISBN-10: 1-55319-376-8

© 2007

Critical Thinking Skills

Simple Machines

Skills For Critical Thinking	Reading Comprehension								Hands-on Activities
	Section 1	Section 2	Section 3	Section 4	Section 5	Section 6	Section 7	Section 8	
LEVEL 1 – Knowledge									
• List Details/Facts	✓	✓	✓	✓		✓	✓	✓	✓
• Recall Information	✓	✓	✓	✓	✓	✓	✓	✓	✓
• Match Vocab. to Definitions	✓	✓	✓		✓				
• Define Vocabulary		✓			✓	✓	✓		
• Label Diagrams				✓		✓	✓		✓
• Recognize Validity (T/F)	✓	✓	✓	✓	✓	✓	✓	✓	
LEVEL 2 – Comprehension									
• Demonstrate Understanding	✓	✓	✓	✓	✓	✓	✓	✓	✓
• Explain Scientific Causation	✓	✓	✓	✓		✓	✓	✓	✓
• Rephrasing Vocab. Meaning	✓	✓	✓	✓		✓			✓
• Describe		✓	✓	✓		✓	✓		✓
• Classify into Scientific Groups	✓	✓	✓	✓	✓	✓	✓	✓	✓
LEVEL 3 – Application									
• Application to Own Life	✓	✓	✓	✓	✓	✓	✓	✓	✓
• Model Scientific Process	✓	✓	✓	✓	✓	✓	✓	✓	✓
• Organize & Classify Facts	✓		✓	✓	✓	✓	✓	✓	✓
• Use Alternative Research Tools									✓
LEVEL 4 – Analysis									
• Distinguish Roles/Meanings									✓
• Make Inferences	✓		✓	✓	✓	✓	✓	✓	✓
• Draw Conclusions Based on Facts Provided	✓		✓	✓	✓	✓			✓
• Classify Based on Facts Researched									✓
LEVEL 5 – Synthesis									
• Compile Research Information									✓
• Design & Application				✓					✓
• Create & Construct				✓	✓				✓
• Imagine self in Scientific Role				✓					✓
LEVEL 6 – Evaluation									
• Defend an Opinion					✓				✓

Based on Bloom's Taxonomy

Contents

• • • • • • • • • • • • • • • •

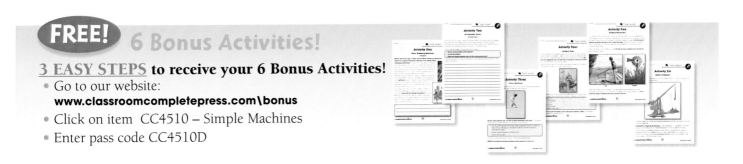

FREE! 6 Bonus Activities!

3 EASY STEPS to receive your 6 Bonus Activities!
• Go to our website:
  www.classroomcompletepress.com\bonus
• Click on item CC4510 – Simple Machines
• Enter pass code CC4510D

Assessment Rubric

Simple Machines

Student's Name: _____ Assignment: _____ Level: _____

	Level 1	Level 2	Level 3	Level 4
Understanding Concepts	Demonstrates a limited understanding of concepts. Requires teacher intervention.	Demonstrates a basic understanding of concepts. Requires little teacher intervention.	Demonstrates a good understanding of concepts. Requires no teacher intervention.	Demonstrates a thorough understanding of concepts. Requires no teacher intervention.
Analysis and Application of Key Concepts	Limited application and interpretation in activity responses	Basic application and interpretation in activity responses	Good application and interpretation in activity responses	Strong application and interpretation in activity responses
Creativity and Imagination	Limited creativity and imagination applied in projects and activities	Some creativity and imagination applied in projects and activities	Satisfactory level of creativity and imagination applied in projects and activities	Beyond expected creativity and imagination applied in projects and activities
Application of Own Interests	Limited application of own interests in independent or group environment	Basic application of own interests in independent or group environment	Good application of own interests in independent or group environment	Strong application of own interests in independent or group environment

STRENGTHS:

WEAKNESSES:

NEXT STEPS:

Teacher Guide

Our resource has been created for ease of use by both *TEACHERS* and *STUDENTS* alike.

Introduction

This resource provides ready-to-use information and activities for remedial students in grades five to eight. Written to grade using simplified language and vocabulary, science concepts are presented in a way that makes them more accessible to students and easier to understand. Comprised of reading passages, student activities and mini posters, our resource can be used effectively for whole-class, small group and independent work.

How Is Our Resource Organized?

STUDENT HANDOUTS

Reading passages and **activities** *(in the form of reproducible worksheets)* make up the majority of our resource. The reading passages present important grade-appropriate information and concepts related to the topic. Embedded in each passage are one or more questions that ensure students understand what they have read.

For each reading passage there are BEFORE YOU READ activities and AFTER YOU READ activities.

- The BEFORE YOU READ activities prepare students for reading by setting a purpose for reading. They stimulate background knowledge and experience, and guide students to make connections between what they know and what they will learn. Important concepts and vocabulary are also presented.

- The AFTER YOU READ activities check students' comprehension of the concepts presented in the reading passage and extend their learning. Students are asked to give thoughtful consideration of the reading passage through creative and evaluative short-answer questions, research, and extension activities.

Hands-on activities are included to further develop students' thinking skills and understanding of the concepts. The **Assessment Rubric** (*page 4*) is a useful tool for evaluating students' responses to many of the activities in our resource. The **Comprehension Quiz** (*page 48*) can be used for either a follow-up review or assessment at the completion of the unit.

PICTURE CUES

Our resource contains three main types of pages, each with a different purpose and use. A **Picture Cue** at the top of each page shows, at a glance, what the page is for.

 Teacher Guide
- Information and tools for the teacher

 Student Handout
- Reproducible worksheets and activities

 Easy Marking™ Answer Key
- Answers for student activities

EASY MARKING™ ANSWER KEY

Marking students' worksheets is fast and easy with this **Answer Key**. Answers are listed in columns – just line up the column with its corresponding worksheet, as shown, and see how every question matches up with its answer!

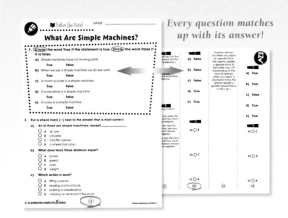

Every question matches up with its answer!

Bloom's Taxonomy

Our resource is an effective tool for any SCIENCE PROGRAM.

Bloom's Taxonomy* for Reading Comprehension

The activities in our resource engage and build the full range of thinking skills that are essential for students' reading comprehension and understanding of important **science concepts**. Based on the six levels of thinking in Bloom's Taxonomy, and using language at a remedial level, information and questions are given that challenge students to not only recall what they have read, but move beyond this to understand the text and concepts through higher-order thinking. By using higher-order skills of application, analysis, synthesis and evaluation, students become active readers, drawing more meaning from the text, attaining a greater understanding of concepts, and applying and extending their learning in more sophisticated ways.

Our resource, therefore, is an effective tool for any **Science** program. Whether it is used in whole or in part, or adapted to meet individual student needs, our resource provides teachers with essential information and questions to ask, inspiring students' interest, creativity, and promoting meaningful learning.

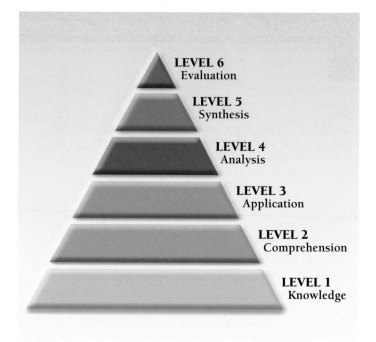

LEVEL 6 Evaluation
LEVEL 5 Synthesis
LEVEL 4 Analysis
LEVEL 3 Application
LEVEL 2 Comprehension
LEVEL 1 Knowledge

BLOOM'S TAXONOMY: 6 LEVELS OF THINKING

Bloom's Taxonomy is a widely used tool by educators for classifying learning objectives, and is based on the work of Benjamin Bloom.

Vocabulary

compound machine	gravity	motion	screw
effort distance	inclined plane	newton	simple machine
effort force	joule	pivot	thread
energy	kinetic energy	potential energy	watt
exert	lever	power	wedge
force	machine	pulley	wheel and axle
friction	meter	resistance distance	work
fulcrum	metric system	resistance force	

NAME: _____

What Are Force, Motion, and Work?

1. **Use a straight line to match the word on the left to its meaning on the right. Use a dictionary to help you.**

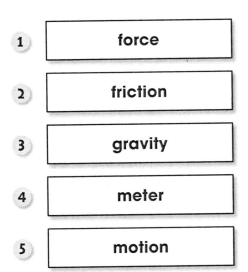

1	force	
2	friction	
3	gravity	
4	meter	
5	motion	

the force of Earth's attraction	A
change of position	B
a measure of distance	C
a push or a pull	D
the force that resists sliding motion	E

2. **Circle the word True if the statement is true. Circle the word False if it is false.**

a) Force is a pull or a push.

True   **False**

b) Friction is the force that makes things fall to the ground.

True   **False**

c) All machines have motors.

True   **False**

d) Changes in motion are caused by forces.

True   **False**

e) Weight is measured in gallons.

True   **False**

NAME: _____

What Are Force, Motion, and Work?

Carrying a 50-pound rock around on your shoulder all day sounds like hard **work**. If you think so, you are half right. It would be hard, but it wouldn't be work—at least not the way the word work is used in science.

To understand what work is we first have to understand **force** and **motion**. You may remember that a force is a push or a pull. You can **exert** a force on something by pushing or pulling with your hands. **Gravity** and **friction** are also common forces.

We can see motion, so we already have a feeling for what it is. When something moves from one place to another, that is motion.

When a force acts on something, it sometimes makes the thing move. If the thing moves *in the direction* that the force is acting, *that* is work. Carrying the rock wasn't work because the force on it was pushing up, and the rock was moving sideways.

Lifting the rock onto your shoulder *is* work. The force is the same as the weight of the rock and the direction of motion is up. Throwing a ball is also work because the ball moves in the direction of the force exerted by your hand.

What Are Force, Motion, and Work?

 here is a way to measure the amount of work done:

Work equals force times distance (W = F X d)

The force is the force that makes something move, and the distance is the total distance the thing moves. Work is measured in foot-pounds. One foot-pound is the work done by exerting one pound of force on something while moving it one foot. If your shoulder is 4 feet high, you do 200 foot-pounds of work when lifting a 50-pound rock to your shoulder (4 X 50 = 200).

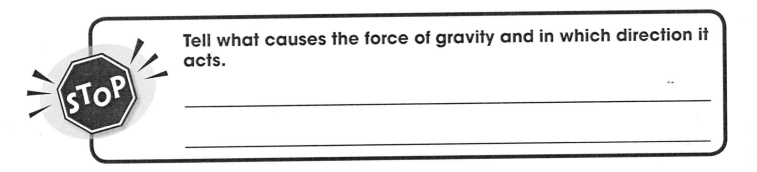

Tell what causes the force of gravity and in which direction it acts.

_____

_____

When you do work on something, you can increase its **energy**. Raising something to a greater height increases its **potential energy**. Making something move faster increases its **kinetic energy**.

In the **metric system**, distance is measured in **meters**, force is measured in **newtons**, and work is measured in **joules**. A meter is about three feet, a newton is about a quarter pound, and a joule is about three-quarters of a foot-pound.

Sometimes you get paid for doing work. When life is fair, your pay depends on how much work you do *and* on how fast you do it. The speed at which work is done is called **power**. Power is measured in joules per second. One joule per second is one **watt**. When you pay your bill to the electric company, you pay for the number of watts of electricity you used.

To find power, divide work by time (P = W ÷ t).

NAME: _____

What Are Force, Motion, and Work?

1. **Put a check mark (✓) next to the answer that is most correct.**

    a) Which are *both* forces?

    ○ **A** work and power
    ○ **B** power and gravity
    ○ **C** gravity and friction
    ○ **D** friction and work

    b) How do you find the amount of work a force does?

    ○ **A** force plus distance
    ○ **B** force times distance
    ○ **C** force minus distance
    ○ **D** force divided by distance

    c) Which word means "the speed at which work is done"?

    ○ **A** force
    ○ **B** power
    ○ **C** kinetic
    ○ **D** energy

    d) What do you need to know to find out how much work you do when you pick up a cat?

    ○ **A** how far you lift the cat and how much it weighs
    ○ **B** how fast you lift the cat and how long you hold it
    ○ **C** how long you hold the cat and how far you walk with it
    ○ **D** how far you walk with the cat and how fast you walk

2. **Circle the words or groups of words that mean "work".**

    force   foot-pounds   force times distance   joules

    watts   newtons   power

After You Read

What Are Force, Motion, and Work?

Answer the questions in complete sentences.

3. Explain why carrying a ten-pound bag of groceries to the car is **not** work.

_____

_____

4. Write a sentence that tells what the words "**distance**," "**force**," and "**work**" have to do with each other..

_____

_____

Extension & Application

5. Nicole planted a new rosebush in her garden. This is what she had to do:

1) She carried the rose bush from her truck to the garden.

2) She dug a hole in the ground.

3) She shoveled the soil from the hole into a wheelbarrow.

4) She wheeled the wheelbarrow full of soil to the street.

5) She pushed the wheelbarrow up a board into the back of a truck and dumped the soil.

a) During which tasks did Nicole **do work**?

_____

b) For each task where she did work, tell what you would need to know to find out **how much** work she did.

_____

_____

_____

_____

_____

NAME: _____

What Are Simple Machines?

1. **Circle** the word True if the statement is true. **Circle** the word False if it is false.

   a) Simple machines have no moving parts.

   True   **False**

   b) When we use a simple machine we do less work.

   True   **False**

   c) A motor scooter is a simple machine.

   True   **False**

   d) A screwdriver is a simple machine.

   True   **False**

   e) A screw is a simple machine.

   True   **False**

2. **Put a check mark (✓) next to the answer that is most correct.**

   a) All of these are simple machines, *except* _____.

   ○ **A** an axe
   ○ **B** a toaster
   ○ **C** a bottle opener
   ○ **D** a wheelchair ramp

   b) What does force times distance equal?

   ○ **A** power
   ○ **B** speed
   ○ **C** work
   ○ **D** weight

   c) Which action is work?

   ○ **A** lifting a pencil
   ○ **B** reading a school book
   ○ **C** pushing a wheelbarrow
   ○ **D** carrying an armload of firewood

What Are Simple Machines?

A **machine** is something that makes work easier by changing the force you apply to do work. A machine can change the amount of force you apply, and it can also change the direction of the force. A **simple machine** is a machine with only one kind of movement.

Wheel and Axle

There are six kinds of simple machines: **lever, wheel and axle, pulley, inclined plane, wedge,** and **screw.** Look at the pictures of the six simple machines. It's easy to see how most of these work and how they change the force. We will look at each of these machines later in this book.

It is important to understand that simple machines make work easier, but they don't change the *amount* of work you have to do. (That's the bad news.) What machines change is the **effort** you have to put out. (That's the good news.)

Inclined Place **Pulley**

For example, you can use a kind of lever to pull a nail out of a board. You could never pull a nail out with your fingers. You might have to push the lever down ten inches to pull the nail up one inch. The nail comes right out because the pull on the nail is ten times the force of your push on the lever.

Wedge **Screw** **Lever**

How does a bottle opener change the force you apply to the handle of the opener?

_____

_____

Later, we will learn more about what you lose and what you gain when you use a simple machine.

What Are Simple Machines?

1. **Circle** the word True if the statement is true. **Circle** the word False if it is false.

   a) A wheel and axle is a simple machine.

       True   **False**

   b) A simple machine has only one kind of motion.

       True   **False**

   c) We use simple machines so we don't have to do as much work.

       True   **False**

   d) A simple machine can change the direction of force.

       True   **False**

   e) A simple machine can change the amount of force.

       True   **False**

2. **Put a check mark (✓) next to the answer that is most correct.**

   a) **Which of these is a simple machine?**

       ○ **A**   bicycle
       ○ **B**   clock
       ○ **C**   pulley
       ○ **D**   toaster

   b) **Which of these is *not* a simple machine?**

       ○ **A**   lamp
       ○ **B**   lever
       ○ **C**   screw
       ○ **D**   wedge

   c) **A simple machine can do all of these things, *except* _____.**

       ○ **A**   change the amount of work
       ○ **B**   change the amount of force
       ○ **C**   change the amount of effort
       ○ **D**   change the direction of force

NAME: _____

What Are Simple Machines?

Answer the questions in complete sentences.

3. Explain what a simple machine is.

_____

_____

4. Name **two** things a simple machine can do.

_____

_____

Extension & Application

5. Name the **six** simple machines and give an example of each.

	Simple Machine	Example
1)		
2)		
3)		
4)		
5)		
6)		

6. When have you used a simple machine? What was it? How did it help you?

_____

_____

NAME: _____

Levers

1. Put a check mark (✓) next to the answer that is most correct.

a) Which tells what a simple machine is?

○ **A** a machine with no motor

○ **B** a machine with no moving parts

○ **C** a machine with one moving part

○ **D** a machine with only one kind of motion

b) What does a simple machine do when it makes your effort less?

○ **A** makes work go faster

○ **B** makes your power more

○ **C** makes the amount of work you do less

○ **D** makes resistance force greater than applied force

c) All of these are simple machines, *except*

○ **A** screw

○ **B** pulley

○ **C** electric fan

○ **D** wheel and axle

2. Circle the word True if the statement is true. Circle the word False if it is false.

a) A lever is a simple machine.

True   **False**

b) Simple machines change the effort needed to do work.

True   **False**

c) Work equals force plus distance.

True   **False**

d) Power is the same as energy.

True   **False**

e) Pounds and newtons measure the same thing.

True   **False**

3. Look up the word PIVOT in a dictionary. Write down its definition below.

The dictionary definition of **pivot** is:

_____

Levers

T he lever was probably the first simple machine used by humans many thousands of years ago. The first person to whack something with a club was using a lever.

The picture shows the two parts of every lever. For every lever, a board or rod **pivots** on a point called a **fulcrum**. The force you apply is called the **effort force**. The lever changes the direction and amount of force and applies it to a load. The force the lever applies is called the **resistance force**. The distance you have to push or pull the lever is called the **effort distance**. The distance the load moves is called the **resistance distance**.

Oars are First-Class Levers

For the oars shown above, the pivot at the edge of the boat (the oarlock) is the fulcrum. The effort force is applied to the oar handle. As the handle moves through the effort distance, it applies the resistance force to the end in the water. The distance

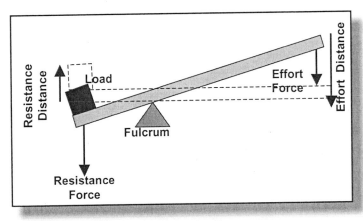

A First-Class Levers

the oar moves through the water is the resistance distance.

There are three kinds of levers because there are three ways to arrange the effort, fulcrum, and load. The oar is a **first-class lever,** where the arrangement is effort-fulcrum-load. Other first-class levers are pliers, scissors, and that little tab you pull to open a can of soft drink.

What are the two parts of every lever?

_____

_____

Levers

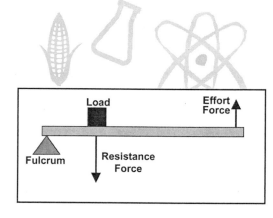

Second-Class Lever

A second-class lever is shown below.

For a second-class lever, the arrangement is effort-load-fulcrum. Some other second-class levers are a wheel barrow and a nutcracker. The classes are just names. It doesn't mean that first-class levers are the best. The third-class lever shown below is just as classy as the others.

For the hammer, the resistance is at the head, and the fulcrum is the back of the hand. Many other **third-class levers** are used to make the resistance force push over a long distance at a high speed. The effort force is large and moves over a shorter distance. This is also how tennis rackets, baseball bats, and brooms work as third-class levers.

A Bottle Opener is a Second-Class Lever

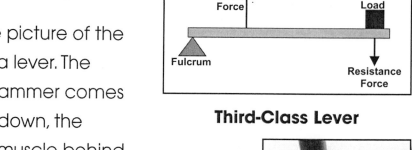

Third-Class Lever

Can you find another lever in the picture of the hammer? The human forearm is a lever. The elbow is the fulcrum. When the hammer comes down, the muscle behind the elbow pulls up. Then it is a first-class lever. When the hammer is lifted up, the muscle in front of the elbow pulls up. Then it is a third-class lever.

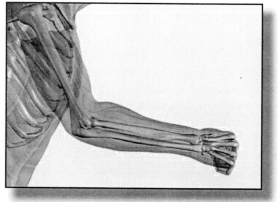

The Forearm is a First-Class Lever and a Third-Class Lever

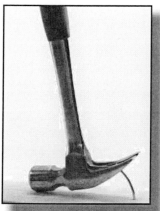

A Hammer is a Third-Class Lever

NAME: _____

Levers

1. Fill in each blank with a word from the list. All words will be used more than once.

effort	fulcrum	resistance

a) A lever pivots on its [_____] .

b) When a lever is used, the load moves through the [_____] distance.

c) The part of a lever that is a board or rod rests on the [_____] .

d) The force applied to a lever is called the [_____] force.

e) The weight of the load on a lever is the [_____] force.

f) The distance you have to push a lever is the [_____] distance.

2. Put a check mark (✓) next to the answer that is most correct.

a) Which tool is most often used as a lever?

○ **A** a nail
○ **B** a knife
○ **C** a wheelchair ramp
○ **D** a bottle opener

b) A second-class lever is shown below.

Load   ▲ Effort Force

What can this lever do?

○ **A** Make less work.
○ **B** Change the direction on the applied force.
○ **C** Make the force on the load greater than the effort force.
○ **D** Make the load move faster than the place where the effort force is applied.

Levers

3. **Answer the questions by writing the answers in the boxes.**

  a) A first-class lever is shown below.

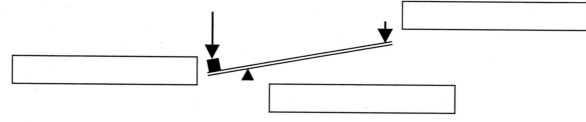

  Label the **effort force,** the **resistance force,** and the **fulcrum.**

  b) A third-class lever is shown below.

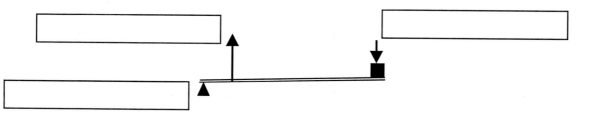

  Label the **effort force,** the **resistance force,** and the **fulcrum.**

Extension & Application

4. **First-class, second-class, and third-class levers are shown below.**

First-Class Lever

Second-Class Lever

Third-Class Lever

Look at the **Three Classes of Levers** chart on the next page. Read the questions for each class of lever. Answer each question by writing YES or NO in the spaces provided.

 After You Read

Three Classes of Levers

Class of Lever	Does the lever make the force greater?	Does the lever change the direction of the force?	Does the lever make the load move faster than the place where the force is applied?	Does the lever make the amount of work less?
First-Class Lever				
Second-Class Lever				
Third-Class Lever				

Wheel and Axles and Pulleys

1. **Circle** the word True if the statement is true. **Circle** the word False if it is false.

   a) All simple machines are basically the same kind of machine.

   True   **False**

   b) Pulleys are simple machines.

   True   **False**

   c) One of the simple machines on a bicycle is a wheel and axle.

   True   **False**

   d) Pulleys can change the direction of force.

   True   **False**

   e) First-class levers are the best kind of levers.

   True   **False**

2. **Put a check mark (✓) next to the answer that is most correct.**

   a) **What is the name of the place where a lever pivots?**

   ○ **A**   fulcrum
   ○ **B**   load
   ○ **C**   pulley
   ○ **D**   wheel

   b) **Which is the same class of lever as a broom?**

   ○ **A**   a boat oar
   ○ **B**   a baseball bat
   ○ **C**   a wheelbarrow
   ○ **D**   a pair of scissors

   c) **Which two things make up a pulley?**

   ○ **A**   a handle and a screw
   ○ **B**   a screw and a wheel
   ○ **C**   a wheel and a rope
   ○ **D**   a rope and a handle

NAME: _____

Wheel and Axles and Pulleys

Wheel and Axle

We will look at wheel and axles next because they are something like levers. The picture below shows how force changes when it is applied to the outside of a wheel.

Pushing or pulling on the wheel turns the axle. The axle doesn't move as far as the wheel but it exerts a large resistance force.

Notice the dotted lines in the picture. This shows how the wheel and axle is also a kind of lever. The effort is applied to the wheel, the axle exerts the resistance force, and the center of the axle is the fulcrum.

Some examples of wheel and axles are doorknobs, screwdrivers, windmills, and waterwheels. Think about any of these things you have seen or used. For example, it is easier to make a screw go into wood if you twist the screwdriver handle than if you twist the bottom part of the screwdriver.

Wheel and axles are often used in a way that is the reverse of the examples. If you apply a large force that spins the axle, the outside of the wheel will spin very fast. This is how the wheels on a car or a bicycle work.

A Wheel and Axle pull on the rope that Raises the Bucket from the Well.

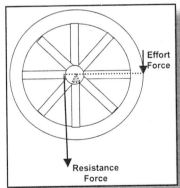

Effort Force

Resistance Force

A wheel and axle can also be seen as a kind of lever. When you think of a wheel and axle this way, where is the fulcrum?

_____

_____

Reading Passage

NAME: _____

Wheel and Axles and Pulleys

Pulleys

 Pulleys use wheels in a different way. Pulley wheels are used to change the direction of force. Also, pulley wheels spin freely around their axles. Different kinds of pulleys are shown below.

Look at the different kinds of pulleys. Pulley number 1 changes the direction of the effort force, but the effort force is equal to the resistance force. With the number 2 set of pulleys, the effort force is only half the resistance force, but you have to pull two feet of rope to raise the load one foot. With the number 3 set of pulleys, the effort force is one-third the resistance force, but you have to pull three feet of rope to raise the load one foot.

Look at the three pulley arrangements again. Count the number of ropes attached to the weight. The more ropes that are attached to the weight, the less force you have to exert and the more rope you have to pull. That's always the way with simple machines. When the machine makes it easier to do something, it also makes you do more of it.

The cords that raise or open window curtains or blinds sometimes run through pulleys. The rope that raises a flag goes over a pulley at the top of the flag pole.

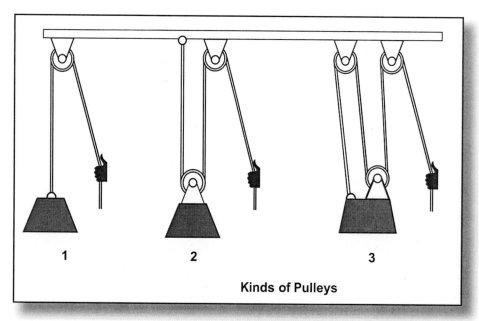

Kinds of Pulleys

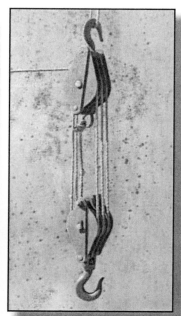

Simple Machines CC4510

NAME: _____

Wheel and Axles and Pulleys

1. **Circle** the word True if the statement is true. **Circle** the word False if it is false.

   a) A screwdriver is a wheel and axle.

   True   **False**

   b) A wheelbarrow is a kind of pulley.

   True   **False**

   c) When a force is applied to a wheel, its axle exerts a greater force.

   True   **False**

   d) A wheel and axle is like a screw.

   True   **False**

   e) A pulley changes the direction of force.

   True   **False**

2. **Put a check mark (✓) next to the answer that is most correct.**

   a) Which of these is a wheel and axle?

   - ○ **A** doorknob
   - ○ **B** hammer
   - ○ **C** nail
   - ○ **D** oar

   b) Which set of pulleys makes it easiest to lift a weight?

   - ○ **A** the one with the longest rope
   - ○ **B** the one with the fewest pulleys
   - ○ **C** the one with the most ropes attached to the weight
   - ○ **D** the one with the least distance between the top and bottom pulleys

   c) Which other simple machine is most like a wheel and axle?

   - ○ **A** lever
   - ○ **B** pulley
   - ○ **C** screw
   - ○ **D** wedge

Wheel and Axles and Pulleys

Answer the questions in complete sentences.

3. **a)** On a wheel and axle, where would you apply force to make a greater force?

    _____

    b) On a wheel and axle, where would you apply force to increase speed?

    _____

4. **a)** The picture shows a pulley, a rope, and a 50-pound weight. Pulling up on the rope raises the weight. How much rope would you have to pull to raise the weight one foot?

    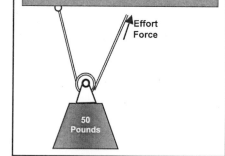

    _____

    b) How much force would it take to raise the weight? Would it take more than, less than, or exactly 50 pounds?

    _____

    Explain how you know. _____

    _____

    _____

Extension & Application

5. Explain how you could use a wheel and axle and a pulley to raise a weight. The wheel and axle and pulley must be combined in a way that makes it possible to raise the weight with less force than if you just lifted it by hand. If you like, you may draw your answer instead of explaining.

    _____

    _____

6. Explain how the combined machines you described above could be used to make the wheel of the wheel and axle spin very fast.

    _____

    _____

NAME: _____

Inclined Planes, Wedges, and Screws

1. **Circle the word True if the statement is true. Circle the word False if it is false.**

   a) A piece of cake is usually in the shape of a wedge.

   True   **False**

   b) A nail is a type of screw.

   True   **False**

   c) Inclined planes are straight up and down.

   True   **False**

   d) A wedge is usually used to split something into two parts.

   True   **False**

   e) An inclined plane has no moving parts.

   True   **False**

2. **Put a check mark (✓) next to the answer that is most correct.**

   a) **A road to the top of a hill is a type of _____.**

   ○ **A** lever
   ○ **B** wedge
   ○ **C** inclined plane
   ○ **D** wheel and axle

   b) **Which of these simple machines are most alike?**

   ○ **A** a pulley and a lever
   ○ **B** a lever and a wheel and axle
   ○ **C** a wheel and axle and a wedge
   ○ **D** a wedge and a pulley

   c) **What does "inclined" mean?**

   ○ **A** bent
   ○ **B** flat
   ○ **C** round
   ○ **D** slanted

NAME: _____

Inclined Planes, Wedges, and Screws

Inclined Planes

An inclined plane is just a slope. It has no moving parts, but it is still called a machine. The pictures show two inclined planes.

One picture shows a loading ramp going into the back of a truck. It is easier to carry a heavy load up the slope than it is to lift it into the truck. It takes longer, but it takes less force. That's how it is with inclined planes. The more gentle the slope, the less effort it takes and the more time it takes.

Loading Ramp

The Basic Wedge Shape

The other picture shows the road to the ancient ruins of Machu Picchu. It's the slow, easy way to the top. Which would you rather do: walk for hours up the inclined plane of the road or climb straight up the hill?

Wheelchair ramps are inclined planes. Any sloping highway or sidewalk is also an inclined plane.

Wedges

A wedge is a simple machine that is a lot like an inclined plane. A wedge is just two inclined planes put together. When you use this machine, the inclined planes move past something instead of moving the thing up a slope.

The Road to Machu Picchu

On the left is the basic shape of a wedge, which is (guess what...) wedge-shaped. The other pictures show a log splitting machine using a wedge to split wood. Other common wedges are axes, knives, and the point of a nail.

STOP

How would you use an inclined plane to increase speed?

_____

_____

Inclined Planes, Wedges, and Screws

Screws

 screw is also a kind of inclined plane. Several kinds of screws are shown below.

Wood Screw   **Bolt and Nut**   **Spiral Staircase**

Three Kinds of Screws

A screw has a groove wound around it the way stripes are wound around a candy cane. The groove is called a **thread.** If you follow one of the grooves, you will find it is one long groove moving from one end to the other. If you could unwind that groove and straighten it out, you would see that it is really one long inclined plane. It's just that this incline has been wrapped around something.

Screws and bolts have this kind of groove. Metal nuts have the same groove on the inside. You couldn't push a screw into wood. With the help of a screwdriver, the thread pulls the screw into the wood as you twist it.

The spiral staircase shown above is also a screw. In this case, it's easy to see that a screw is really an inclined plane going up and around in circles. With a wood screw, the screw moves when you use it. With a spiral staircase, the screw sits still, and you move.

Inclined Planes, Wedges, and Screws

1. **Circle** the word True if the statement is true. **Circle** the word False if it is false.

   a) A wedge is like two inclined planes put together.

   True   **False**

   b) A spiral staircase is like a very large lever.

   True   **False**

   c) Wedges and inclined planes can be seen as types of screws.

   True   **False**

   d) Pushing a wedge through something changes a downward force into two sideways forces.

   True   **False**

   e) The grooves on a screw are called needles.

   True   **False**

2. Tell whether these things are inclined planes, wedges, or screws. In the space beside the name of each thing, write **IP** for INCLINED PLANE, **W** for WEDGE, or **S** for SCREW.

   _____ **a)** spiral staircase

   _____ **b)** wheelchair ramp

   _____ **c)** threaded bolt

   _____ **d)** knife

   _____ **e)** path to the top of a hill

   _____ **f)** axe

NAME: _____

Inclined Planes, Wedges, and Screws

Answer the questions in complete sentences.

3. Explain why a **screw** is a kind of inclined plane.

_____

_____

4. When you walk up an inclined plane, like a hill, your legs supply the effort force. What is the **resistance force**?

_____

_____

5. When the wedge of an axe head splits a log, what are the **directions** of the effort force and the resistance forces? (There two resistance forces.)

_____

_____

Extension & Application

6. The spiral staircase, shown here, is a kind of screw.

a) The staircase is 50 feet high. You have to go around 5 times to get to the top. Each time you go around, you walk 30 feet and get 10 feet higher. How far do you have to walk to get to the top? _____

Suppose there was a 50-foot ladder beside the staircase. The ladder goes straight up.

b) What would you gain by using the ladder? _____

c) What you gain by using the stairs? _____

d) Do you do less work when you take the stairs? Explain. _____

e) How could you develop more power by taking the ladder? _____

_____

Before You Read   NAME: _____

Compound Machines

1. **Circle** the word True if the statement is true. **Circle** the word False if it is false.

   a) Compound means separate.

         True   **False**

   b) A wedge is a simple machine.

         True   **False**

   c) We can do some things with simple machines we couldn't do without them.

         True   **False**

   d) An axe is made of two simple machines.

         True   **False**

   e) Simple machines are always smaller than machines with motors.

         True   **False**

2. **Put a check mark (✓) next to the answer that is most correct.**

   a) **Which simple machine is a bottle opener?**

   ○ **A** lever
   ○ **B** pulley
   ○ **C** inclined plane
   ○ **D** wheel and axle

   b) **Which simple machine is a windmill?**

   ○ **A** pulley
   ○ **B** wedge
   ○ **C** inclined plane
   ○ **D** wheel and axle

   c) **Which simple machine is a knife?**

   ○ **A** lever
   ○ **B** pulley
   ○ **C** screw
   ○ **D** wedge

Simple Machines CC4510

Compound Machines

A compound machine is a machine that combines two or more simple machines to do one job. The things we usually call machines, like cars, have many simple machines working together in complicated ways. A bicycle is simpler than a car, but it is also made up of simple machines. The moving parts include several wheel and axles, levers, and pulleys.

An axe is a compound machine.

The handle is a lever, and the head is a wedge.

Axe

The wire cutter is a compound machine. The handles are levers and the cutting edges are wedges.

Wire cutter

The C-clamp is a combination of a lever and a screw.

The can opener combines three simple machines.

A wedge cuts into the can, the handles are levers that force the cutter down, and a wheel and axle moves the cutter around the edge of the can.

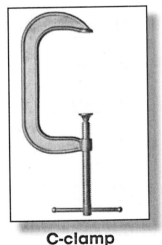

C-clamp

Can opener

The posthole digger shown below is a compound machine.

To dig a hole, you first push the blades into the ground. Then you pull the handles apart to grip the soil between the blades and pull up to get the soil out of the hole. Which two simple machines are parts of the posthole digger?

_____

_____

NAME: _____

Compound Machines

1. **Circle** the word True if the statement is true. **Circle** the word False if it is false.

   a) A compound machine is a simple machine with a motor.

   True   **False**

   b) A bicycle is a compound machine.

   True   **False**

   c) An axe is a wedge and a lever.

   True   **False**

   d) A pulley is a compound machine because it has a wheel and a rope.

   True   **False**

2. A can opener is shown below.

   When you squeeze the handles of the can opener together, a blade cuts through the top of the can. When you spin the knob around, the can opener moves around the edge of the can, cutting through the top as it goes. In the boxes, name the **three simple machines** that are parts of this compound machine.

   a) The knob is a

   _____

   b) The handles are

   _____

   c) The blade is a

   _____

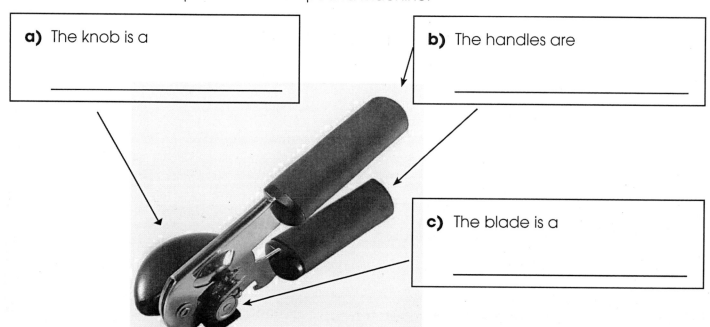

After You Read

Compound Machines

Answer the questions in complete sentences.

3. Name **two** compound machines. For each machine you name, tell which simple machines are parts of the compound machine.

   a) Name of compound machine: _____

   Simple machines: _____

   _____

   _____

   b) Name of compound machine: _____

   Simple machines: _____

   _____

Extension & Application

4. The bicycle shown below is a compound machine.

Find as many simple machines as you can that are parts of the bicycle. Label each part you find with the name of the simple machine and draw **arrows** pointing to them. You should be able to find **at least three** different simple machines.

NAME: _____

Gains and Losses with Simple Machines

1. Put a check mark (✓) next to the answer that is most correct.

a) Simple machines can do all of these things for us, *except* give us

_____.

- ○ **A** less work
- ○ **B** more force
- ○ **C** more speed
- ○ **D** force in a different direction

b) Which measures how fast we do work?

- ○ **A** power
- ○ **B** force
- ○ **C** speed
- ○ **D** energy

c) What is a simple machine?

- ○ **A** a model of a real machine
- ○ **B** a machine without a motor
- ○ **C** a machine with no moving parts
- ○ **D** a machine with only one kind of motion

2. Circle the word True if the statement is true. Circle the word False if it is false.

a) Simple machines can give us more force.

    True   **False**

b) Some simple machines have moving parts.

    True   **False**

c) Simple machines always make us use more effort.

    True   **False**

d) When a simple machine makes work easier, it usually takes longer to do the work.

    True   **False**

e) A lever is a compound machine.

    True   **False**

Gains and Losses with Simple Machines

We have studied all six simple machines: lever, wheel and axle, pulley, inclined plane, wedge, and screw.

We saw that the wheel and axle works much like a lever. A wheel and axle is sort of a spinning lever. We also saw that inclined planes, wedges, and screws are a lot alike. A wedge is a double inclined plane that moves and forces things apart. A screw is a long inclined plane wrapped round and round.

Simple machines can do three things to the force we apply when doing work. They can change the direction of force, they can make the force greater, and they can make the force less. Machines can also change the direction of

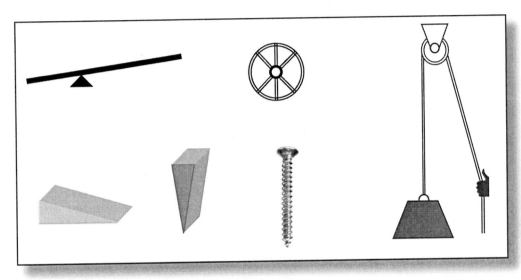

motion and make it faster or slower. We use simple machines because we want one of these changes. We always pay for it with one of the other changes we don't want, but we decide it is a good trade for what we get.

Remember, simple machines don't change the amount of work; they just make it easier. We can raise a 200-pound rock by pushing down on a lever with a force of only 50 pounds. We pay for that gain by having to push down 4 feet to raise the rock 1 foot. Remember, work equals force times distance. The work we put in (4 X 50 = 200 foot-pounds) is the same as the work that gets done (1 X 200 = 200 foot-pounds). Still you win. Most people can't lift a 200-pound rock. So the lever gives you a way to do something you couldn't do without it.

How many foot-pounds of work do you do when you lift ten 5-pound bricks up three feet into the back of a truck?

_____

_____

Gains and Losses with Simple Machines

Many kinds of levers are used to increase the speed of something by exerting a lot of force. When someone swings an axe to chop a log, they are using a lot of force at one end of a lever to increase the speed of the axe head at the other end. The axe head can hit a log so hard it splits in half.

With most simple machines the trade is like this:

This is what you gain: You put out a little force and something moves. The force you exert is less than the force it would take to move the thing without the machine.

This is what you lose: You have to exert the force for a longer time and over a longer distance.

So you exchange hard and quick for easy and slow.

You turn a wheel easily for a long distance, and the axle exerts a lot of force. You give a long, easy pull on a rope and a set of pulleys raises a heavy weight.

You take a long easy stroll up an incline and move a few feet higher.

You pound an 8-inch wedge into a log, and a 1-inch crack appears in the log.

You twist a screwdriver handle many times, and a screw goes down into a board one inch.

You can do things with simple machines you couldn't do without them. It just takes a while.

Gains and Losses with Simple Machines

1. **Circle** the word True if the statement is true. **Circle** the word False if it is false.

   a) You can do some things with simple machines that you couldn't do without them.

   True   **False**

   b) If a simple machine makes something easier, it always makes it quicker too.

   True   **False**

   c) When we gain something with a simple machine, we always lose something too.

   True   **False**

   d) When you swing an axe to chop a log or swing a bat to hit a ball, what you gain is speed.

   True   **False**

   e) The easier it is to lift something with a set of pulleys, the less rope you have to pull to do it.

   True   **False**

2. **Put a check mark (✓) next to the answer that is most correct.**

   a) A wheel and axle works a lot like a _____.

   ○ **A** lever
   ○ **B** pulley
   ○ **C** screw
   ○ **D** wedge

   b) Which simple machines are like kinds of inclined planes?

   ○ **A** pulley and wedge
   ○ **B** wedge and screw
   ○ **C** screw and lever
   ○ **D** lever and pulley

   c) Simple machines can do all of these things, *except* _____.

   ○ **A** make force greater
   ○ **B** make motion faster
   ○ **C** make the amount of work less
   ○ **D** make force act in a different direction

Gains and Losses with Simple Machines

Answer the questions in complete sentences.

3. Some simple machines make the force you apply much greater. Give an example of a machine that makes applied force greater and explain the motion that happens.

    _____

    _____

4. For the machine you named in Question 3 above, tell what you give up or lose in exchange for the greater force you get.

    _____

    _____

Extension & Application

5. Look at the chart on the next page, **Direction of Motion in Simple Machines.** It shows three kinds of **levers** and four other **simple machines.**

    a) In each picture, the arrows show **how** the machine moves when an effort force is applied. **Show** how this applied force causes another motion somewhere else. The question marks are where the other motion happens. Next to the question mark is an arrow stem with no point.

    Put the points on the arrows to show the direction of the <u>motion</u>. *Remember* you are showing the direction of motion, *not* direction of a force.

    b) Which of the simple machines in the chart change the direction of motion?

    _____

    _____

    _____

    _____

NAME: _____

Direction of Motion in Simple Machines

First-Class Lever

Second-Class Lever

Third-Class Lever

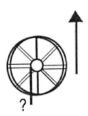

Wheel

Screw

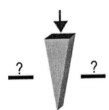

Wedge

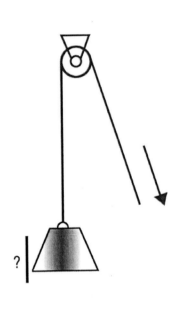

Pulley

First-Class Levers

In this activity you will study how the DISTANCES and FORCES all work together for a first-class lever.

This is what you will need:

- A 12-inch wooden ruler
- Something to use for a fulcrum—a pencil will do
- A handful of pennies

All pennies have about the same weight. You can use the number of pennies to measure the amount of weight.

This is what you do:

1. Lay the ruler crossways on the pencil.
2. Put two pennies on one end of the ruler and one penny on the other end.
3. Slide the ruler across the pencil until it balances.
4. See how many inches are on each side of the fulcrum (the pencil).

Repeat these four steps with different amounts of pennies on each end. Each time you do it, write down the distances and numbers of pennies. Can you find a pattern to the weights and distances? See if your weights and distances fit this equation:

(pennies on left) X (left side distance) = (pennies on right) X (right side distance)

We can think of pennies as **weight,** and weight is **force.** So what all this means is that, "Resistance force times resistance distance equals effort force times effort distance." Even more simply, it means, "Work in equals work out."

A Pocketful of Simple Machines

This activity is about all the simple machines found in a Swiss Army knife. A picture of this kind of pocketknife is shown below. You can use the picture, but, if you can get a Swiss Army knife to look at, it would be easier.

See how many different SIMPLE MACHINES you can find in a Swiss Army knife. See if you can find any COMPOUND MACHINES. There are many different kinds of these knives, so you will not all get the same answers. Some knives have even more gadgets that pop out than the one shown.

_____

_____

_____

_____

_____

_____

Machine Hunt Game

This game is played with two or more people. You will hunt for one example of each of the different kinds of simple machines in your home or at school. The winner is the person to find **all six** simple machines first. Set a time limit of 20 or 30 minutes. If no one has found all six when the time is up, then whoever has found the most simple machines wins.

Remember that the SIX SIMPLE MACHINES are:

inclined plane

wedge

lever

wheel and axle

pulley

screw

Set some boundaries, like inside your house. The kitchen is a good place to start. A toy box or tool box are also good places to look. Look carefully. You will probably find some simple machines in places you never expected to find them!

Good luck, and have fun hunting!

Visit a Hardware Store

You can find all the **SIMPLE MACHINES** in a hardware store. Visit a large hardware store and look for or ask to see these things:

- Wrenches, crowbars, and Wonderbars
- A drain snake, screwdrivers, doorknobs
- Pulleys
- Loading ramps or wheel ramps for raising cars (You might have to go to an auto parts store to see these.)
- Wedges (for splitting logs)
- Many different kinds of screws

You should be able to recognize which simple machine each of these is. Look around for other tools that are simple machines.

You should see a lot of COMPOUND MACHINES too. Look among the hand tools. Look for clamps, vices, bolt cutters, pipe wrenches, Yankee drills, brace and bits, and vice grips. Try to find a compound machine called a "come-along". This machine increases your force so much you can move a car with one hand!

Write down each machine you find. Record the name, whether it is a simple machine or a compound machine, and draw a sketch to show what it looks like. Record your findings in a chart like the one below.

Name	Simple machine or compound machine?	Sketch

Crossword Puzzle!

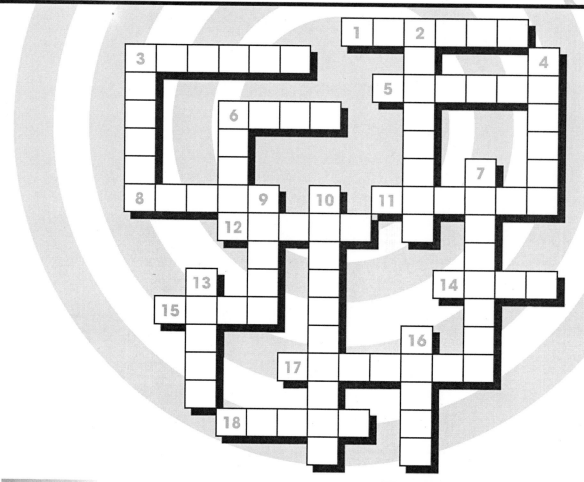

Across

1. The force you apply to a simple machine is the _____ force.
3. With a rope and a wheel, you can make a _____.
5. A machine with only one kind of movement is a _____ machine.
6. Force times distance.
8. A spiral staircase is a kind of _____.
11. A change from one place to another.
12. You can make one with a board and a fulcrum.
14. One joule per second.
15. Wheel and _____.
17. Something to do work with less effort.
18. A push or a pull.

Down

2. The force that slows down something that is sliding.
3. Ramps are inclined _____.
4. How force is measured in the metric system.
6. _____ and axle.
7. How far a lever moves the load is the resistance _____.
9. The simple machine that looks like a piece of cake.
10. The load on a lever is the _____ force.
13. To apply a force is to _____ a force.
16. What levers do on their fulcrums.

Simple Machines CC4510

NAME: _____

Word Search

Find all of the words in the Word Search. Words are written horizontally, vertically, diagonally, and some are even written backwards.

AXLE	RESISTANCE	EXERT	PIVOT	WHEEL
METER	ENERGY	NEWTON	WEDGE	LEVER
PULLEY	MOTION	WATT	FULCRUM	POWER
DISTANCE	SCREW	FORCE	PLANE	WORK
METRIC				

B	W	H	E	E	L	C	D	T	F	S	E
G	A	N	H	C	R	J	R	K	E	C	N
K	T	O	L	M	N	E	N	P	N	R	E
R	T	I	E	L	X	A	W	A	A	E	R
O	Q	T	R	E	S	R	T	O	L	W	G
W	F	O	R	C	E	S	T	S	P	V	Y
E	W	M	X	V	I	Y	Z	I	I	B	E
D	C	D	E	S	F	R	V	G	H	D	L
G	J	L	E	K	N	O	T	W	E	N	L
E	L	R	M	E	T	E	R	E	M	N	U
P	Q	R	F	U	L	C	R	U	M	S	P

NAME: _____

Comprehension Quiz

25

Part A

7

Circle the word True if the statement is true. Circle the word False if it is false.

1) When a force causes something to move, work is done.

   True   **False**

2) Work is power.

   True   **False**

3) A candle is a simple machine.

   True   **False**

4) A lever pivots on its fulcrum.

   True   **False**

5) A doorknob is a wheel and axle.

   True   **False**

6) A wedge is a kind of lever.

   True   **False**

7) We don't have to do as much work when we use a simple machine.

   True   **False**

Part B

Put a check mark (✓) next to the answer that is most correct.

3

1. Which two things do we need to know to find how much work is done?
   - **A** time and distance
   - **B** distance and force
   - **C** force and energy
   - **D** energy and time

2. Which of these simple machines usually doesn't move when it is being used?
   - **A** lever
   - **B** pulley
   - **C** inclined plane
   - **D** wheel and axle

3. Which of these is a simple machine?
   - **A** match
   - **B** pencil
   - **C** watch
   - **D** wedge

SUBTOTAL: /10

Simple Machines CC4510

NAME: _____

Part C

Answer each question in complete sentences.

1. Name the **six simple machines** and give an example of each. ⑥

    a) Name: _____

    example: _____

    b) Name: _____

    example: _____

    c) Name: _____

    example: _____

    d) Name: _____

    example: _____

    e) Name: _____

    example: _____

    f) Name: _____

    example: _____

2. Name **one compound machine** and tell which simple machines it is made of. ③

    _____

    _____

3. Tell **two** things a simple machine can do to applied force. ③

    _____

    _____

4. Which **two** simple machines are most like an inclined plane? ③

    _____

    _____

SUBTOTAL: /15

1.

a) True

b) True

c) False

d) True

e) True

2.

a) ◉ C

b) ◉ A

c) ◉ A

⑭

Answers will vary (i.e. When you apply an upward force, the opener applies a greater force to the bottle cap. OR (Depending on the type of opener) when you apply a downward force, the opener applies a greater upward force to the cap.)

⑬

1.

a) False

b) False

c) False

d) True

e) True

2.

a) ◉ B

b) ◉ C

c) ◉ A

⑫

3.

Answers will vary (i.e. The force is upward, but the motion is sideways.)

4.

Work equals force times distance.

5.

a) Tasks 2, 3, and 5

b) Task 2: how deep the hole was and how much the soil weighed.

Task 3: how high the wheelbarrow was and how much the soil weighed.

Task 5: how high the truck bed was and how much the wheelbarrow and soil together weighed.

⑪

Answers will vary (i.e. Gravity is caused by the attraction between the mass of an object and the mass of the Earth. It acts downward or toward Earth's surface.)

⑨

1.

a) ◉ C

b) ◉ B

c) ◉ B

d) ◉ A

2.

Circle

foot-pounds

force times distance

joules

⑩

1.

D ①

E ②

A ③

C ④

B ⑤

2.

a) True

b) False

c) False

d) True

e) False

⑦

1.
a) True
b) False
c) True
d) False
e) True

2.
a) ⊘ A
b) ⊘ C
c) ⊘ A

(25)

1.
a) False
b) True
c) True
d) True
e) False

2.
a) ⊘ A
b) ⊘ B
c) ⊘ C

(22)

The center of the axle.

(23)

3.
a) **Left to right**
resistance force, fulcrum, effort force

b) **Top left:**
effort force.
Bottom left:
fulcrum.
Right:
resistance force.

4.
First-class: Y, Y, N, N
Second-class: Y, N, N, N
Third-class: N, N, Y, N

(20)

Answers will vary
(i.e. A board or
rod and a pivot or
fulcrum.)

(17)

1.
a) fulcrum
b) resistance
c) fulcrum
d) effort
e) resistance
f) effort

2.
a) ⊘ D
b) ⊘ C

(19)

1.
a) ⊘ D
b) ⊘ D
c) ⊘ C

2.
a) True
b) True
c) False
d) False
e) True

3.
Accept any
reasonable answer.

(16)

3.
A simple machine is a
machine with one kind
of motion.

4.
Answers will vary
(i.e. Change amount
of force, change
direction of force,
change direction of
motion, increase force,
decrease force.)

5.
In any order:
lever – Answers will
vary (i.e. hammer,
bottle opener,
crowbar).
wheel and axle –
Answers will vary
(i.e. pump windlass,
bicycle wheel).
pulley – Answers will
vary (i.e. flag pole
rope).
inclined plane –
Answers will vary (i.e.
wheelchair ramp).
wedge – Answers will
vary (i.e. knife, axe).
screw – Answers will
vary (i.e. wood screw,
corkscrew, bolt).

6.
Answers will vary.

(15)

1.
a) False
b) True
c) True
d) False

2.
a) wheel and axle
b) levers
c) wedge

(34)

1.
a) False
b) True
c) True
d) True
e) False

2.
a) ◉ A
b) ◉ D
c) ◉ D

(32)

Two wedges and two levers.

(33)

---

3. Answers will vary
(i.e. It is a slope wrapped round and round.)

4. Gravity

5. The effort force is down and the resistance forces are sideways.

6.
a) 150 feet
b) Less distance
c) Less effort
d) No, because the vertical distance is the same.
e) If you went up the ladder faster you would develop more power.

(31)

1.
a) True
b) False
c) False
d) True
e) False

2.
a) S
b) IP
c) S
d) W
e) IP
f) W

(30)

1.
a) True
b) False
c) False
d) True
e) True

2.
a) ◉ C
b) ◉ B
c) ◉ D

(27)

Answers will vary.
(i.e. Go from the top to the bottom. OR Roll something down from the top.)

(28)

3.
a) You would apply it to the outside of the wheel.
b) You would apply it to the axle.

4.
a) two feet
b) It would take less force than 50 pounds because two ropes come from the load, OR You have to pull a greater length of rope than the weight rises, OR The effort force is less than the resistance force. (Answers will vary.)

5. Answers will vary
(i.e. Tie the rope to the weight. Hang to pulley overhead. Put the rope over the pulley. Tie the other end to the axle. Spin the wheel and wind up the rope.)

6. Answers will vary
(i.e. Let the weight drop from above up near the pulley. The rope will unwind from the axle and spin the wheel.)

(26)

3.

Answers will vary (i.e. A lever makes force greater. You push down on one end and the other end pushes up with a greater force. OR You spin the outside of a wheel and the axle applies greater force as it spins.)

4.

Answers will vary (i.e. Lever – You have to push farther than the load moves. Wheel and axle – The axle doesn't move as far as you move the wheel.)

40

5.

a)

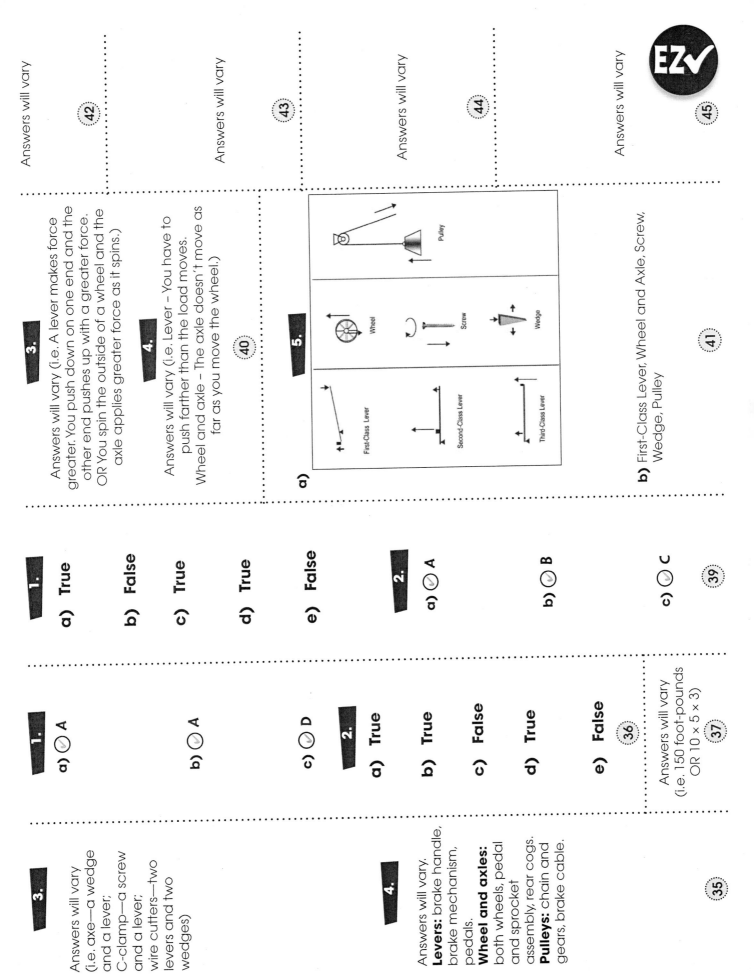

First-Class Lever

Second-Class Lever

Third-Class Lever

Wheel

Screw

Wedge

Pulley

41

b) First-Class Lever, Wheel and Axle, Screw, Wedge, Pulley

1.

a) True

b) False

c) True

d) True

e) False

2.

a) ◯ A

b) ◯ B

c) ◯ C

39

1.

a) ◯ A

b) ◯ A

c) ◯ D

2.

a) True

b) True

c) False

d) True

e) False

36

Answers will vary
(i.e. 150 foot-pounds
OR 10 × 5 × 3)

37

3.

Answers will vary
(i.e. axe—a wedge
and a lever;
C-clamp—a screw
and a lever;
wire cutters—two
levers and two
wedges)

4.

Answers will vary.
Levers: brake handle,
brake mechanism,
pedals.
Wheel and axles:
both wheels, pedal
and sprocket
assembly, rear cogs.
Pulleys: chain and
gears, brake cable.

35

© CLASSROOM COMPLETE PRESS

Simple Machines CC4510

Word Search Answers

Across:

1. effort
3. pulley
5. simple
6. work
8. screw
11. motion
12. lever
14. watt
15. axle
17. machine
18. force

Down:

2. friction
3. planes
4. newton
6. wheel
7. distance
9. wedge
10. resistance
13. exert
16. pivot

Part A

1) True
2) False
3) False
4) True
5) True
6) False
7) False

Part B

1) ✓ B
2) ✓ C
3) ✓ D

Part C

1.

In any order:

lever –
Answers will vary
(i.e. bottle opener).

wheel and axle –
Answers will vary
(i.e. doorknob).

pulley –
Answers will vary
(i.e. flagpole rope).

inclined plane –
Answers will vary
(i.e. wheelchair ramp).

wedge –
Answers will vary
(i.e. knife).

screw –
Answers will vary
(i.e. corkscrew).

2.
Answers will vary
(i.e. axe, made of lever
and wedge)

3.
Answers will vary
(i.e. increase force,
decrease force, change
direction of force)

4.
wedge and screw

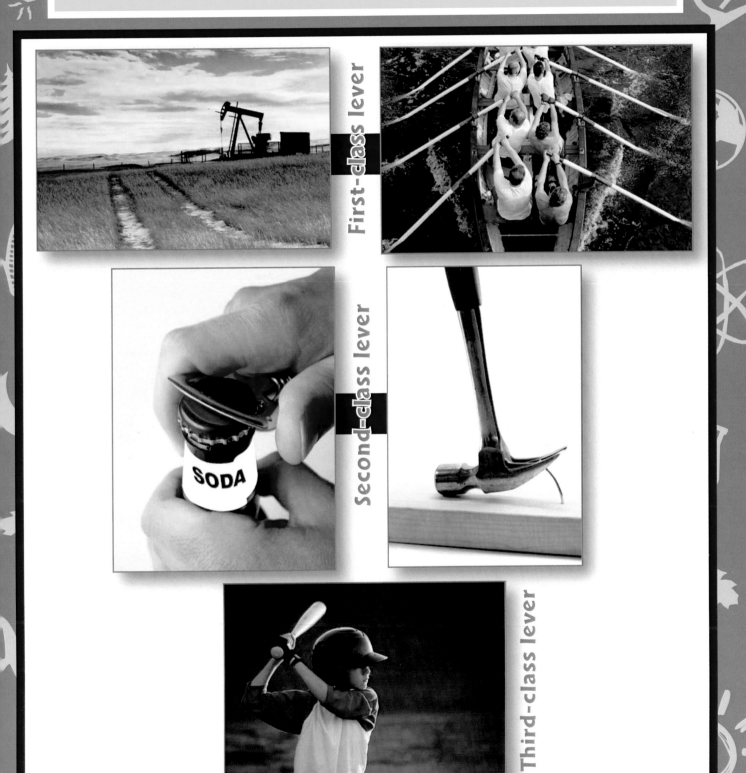

First-class lever

Second-class lever

Third-class lever

SODA

Pulleys and Wheel and Axles

Crane

Pulley

Pulley

Ships wheel

Steering wheel

Wheel & Axle

Axe - Wedge

Ramp - Incline Plane

Knife - Wedge

Inclined Plane

Spike - Wedge

Road - Incline Plane

Simple Machines CC4510

Screws

Bolt

Spiral Staircase

Drill Bit

Cork screw

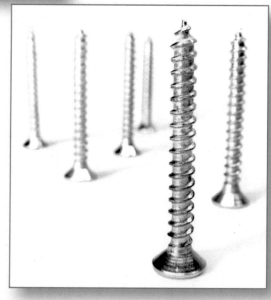

Screw

Bicycle - A Compound Machine

Mountain Bike

Compound Machines

Can Opener

Clamp

Wire Cutters

Swiss Army Knife